Elementary Grade Two
Workbook

Our Prophet Muhammad

Salla Allahu alaihi wa sallam

Life in Makkah

Dr. Tasneema Ghazi
Rahayu Mohammad

 IQRA' International Educational Foundation

Part of a Comprehensive, Integrated and Systematic Program of Islamic Studies

A Workbook for the program of *Sirah* Elementary Level Grade-2

Our Prophet: Workbook: part One

Chief Program Editors
Dr. Abidullah Ghazi
(Ph.D., Study of Religion
Harvard University)

Dr. Tasneema Ghazi
(Ph.D., Curriculum-Reading
University of Minnesota)

Editing
Huseyin Abiva

Maps
Huseyin Abiva

Design
Robinson Design
Aliuddin Khaja

First printed in December, 2008
Printed in U.S.A

ISBN # 1-56316-185-0

IQRA' Notes

It is our pleasure to present this new, completely revised and expanded edition of IQRA's popular *Sirah* series, Our Prophet Muhammad ﷺ. This workbook, used in conjunction with its accompanying textbook, is especially prepared to enhance students' understanding of the *Sirah* of the Blessed Messenger of God ﷺ and bring them closer to his noble personality.

The skills and readability level of this workbook have been carefully evaluated to be appropriate for new readers. It is our hope that students will be able to grasp the concepts introduced in each lesson and receive the opportunity to master Islamic concepts and models.

Workbooks are an integral part of IQRA's educational program. It is recommended that teachers use the workbooks in conjunction with the textbook during the class. This workbook has been prepared to provide pupils with important exercises in comprehension and to aid in the development of critical thinking skills.

We invite you to join hands in our efforts by sending us your comments and suggestions. Let's begin to build a viable and professional program of Islamic education for our future generations with the Grace of God and the love of His Messenger ﷺ!

Chief Editors
December, 2008

Table of Contents

Table of Contents

Activity 1

Fill in the blanks with the correct words in the brackets.

1. People who follow Islam are called _meslim_.

   (Christians, Muslims, Hindus)

2. Muslims believe in Allah, the _one_ and Only God.

   (One, Two, Three)

3. Prophet Muhammad is our _Rasullalon_

   (Angel, Rasulullah, Jinn)

4. Allah has sent us _many_ prophets and messengers.

   (Many, one, a few)

5. The first prophet is _adam_ and the last prophet is Muhammad.

   (Jibril, Adam, Ibrahim)

6. The last message is the _Qieron_, which Allah gave to Rasulullah.

   (*Hadith*, dictionary, Qur'an)

7. We are the *Ummah* of Rasulullah. To show that we love him, we follow his _Suhhah_.

   (Smile, *Sunnah*, *Salah*)

Activity 2

Select the correct word given below and write it in the box where it belongs

Religions   Prophets   Books of Allah   Places of worship

Qur'an,
Zabur, Injil

Qur'an

Adam ﷺ
Muhammad ﷺ
Ibrahim ﷺ

mohammod (s)

Islam,
Christianity,
Judaism

islom

Mosque,
Church,
Synagogue

mosque

Activity 3

Muhammad ﷺ is our Prophet. We are his *Ummah*. We believe Allah ﷻ is the only God and Muhammad ﷺ is Rasulullah.

Muslims live all over the world. On the map below, color each continent a different color.

Our World

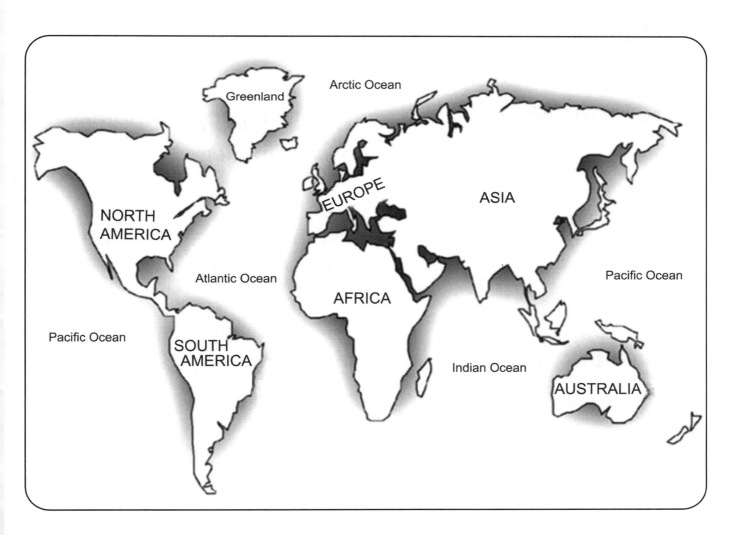

Activity 4

Use the same color (red, blue, green, or yellow) to match the words to its meaning.

Ummah   The message from Allah ﷻ to the people of the world

Qur'an   Allah's Messenger ﷺ

Rasulullah ﷺ   A group of people who have the same beliefs

Allah ﷻ   Muslim believes He is the One and Only God

Sunnah   The teachings and actions of Rasulullah ﷺ

We Love Our Prophet ﷺ

Activity 1

Read and check the correct sentences in the box.

1. Muhammad ﷺ is our Prophet.
   - ▲ He is Allah's last Prophet.
   - ▲ He is Allah's first Prophet.

2. All Muslims love Rasulullah ﷺ.
   - ▲ He was good and kind to everyone.
   - ▲ He was good and kind only to the Muslims.

3. Allah ﷻ is happy if we obey Rasulullah ﷺ.
   - ▲ He will take care of us here and in the *Akhirah*.
   - ▲ He will leave us alone.

4. Allah ﷻ and His angels bless us when…
   - ▲ We send flowers to Rasulullah ﷺ.
   - ▲ We send *Salawat* on Rasulullah ﷺ.

5. We follow the sayings of Rasulullah ﷺ when….
   - ▲ We follow the *Ahadith*.
   - ▲ We follow the Qur'an.

Activity 2

Think, follow the arrows and then write the 'effect' of following actions in the spaces below.

Cause		Effect

Cause   **Effect**

_____sunah_____

We follow Rasulullah ﷺ ➡ _____
                            _____

We follow Allah ﷻ ➡ _____
                        _____
                        _____

We send *Salawat*
on Rasulullah ﷺ ➡ _____
                      _____
                      _____

We learn the *Ahadith* ➡ _____
                            _____
                            _____

Activity 3

Using the words below plan an activity you can do to follow Rasulullah's example. Draw or paste a picture of your activities in the following spaces.

help others   obey my uncle   donate money   pray

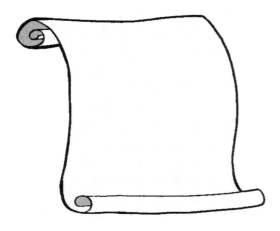

I can _pray_

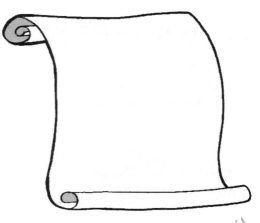

I can _donaT manay_

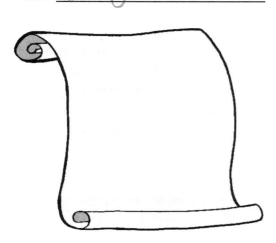

I can _help oTher_

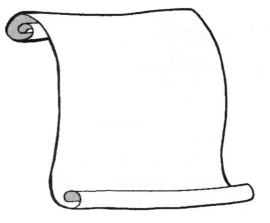

I can _obey my uncle_

Activity 4

Choose the word which does not belong in each line.
Write the first letter of this word in the space next to it.

Ibrahim ➯ Allah ➯ Ismail ➯ **A**

Hadith ➯ Qur'an ➯ Injil ➯ Q

boy ➯ angel ➯ girl ➯ b

first ➯ last ➯ door ➯ F

husband ➯ *imam* ➯ wife ➯ I

Ka'bah ➯ *masjid* ➯ temple ➯ K

short ➯ tall ➯ house ➯ h

When all completed, the letters will spell a word. Can you guess?

— — — — — — —

The Arabian Peninsula

Lesson 3

Activity 1

The sentences below tell you about Makkah and Madinah.

TRUE or FALSE? Write the answer on the lines.

1. Makkah is the birth place of Rasulullah ﷺ.   F

2. The Ka'bah is built in Makkah.   F

3. The first *Ayahs* were sent down in Madinah.   F

4. Madinah is called the 'City of the Prophet".   T

5. Masjid an-Nabawi was built in Makkah.   F

6. Rasulullah ﷺ died after ten years of living in Madinah.   F

9

Activity 2

The map below shows the Arabian Peninsula. Study the map. Then circle the best answer for each question.

Arabian Peninsula

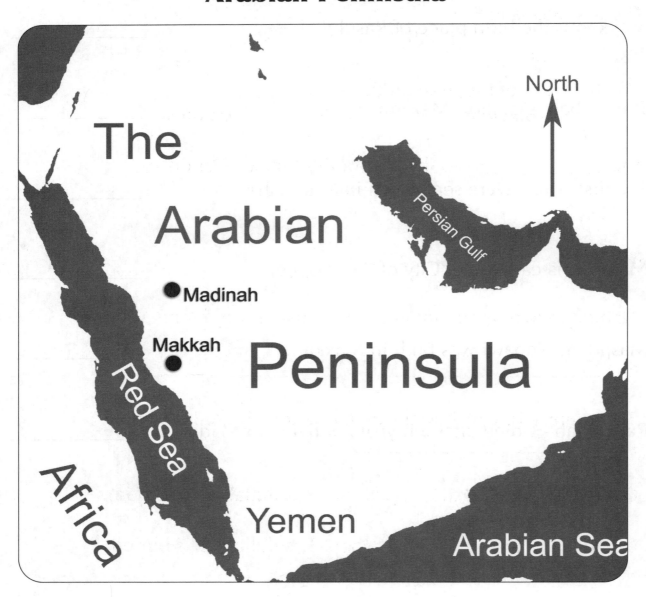

Activity 3

PART A.

1. A peninsula is surrounded by water on _____ sides

           two   three   five

2. The Red Sea is to the _____of the Arabian Peninsula.

          north   east   west

3. On the south of the Arabian Peninsula is_____.

     Black Sea   Arabian Sea   Dead Sea

4. The _____is to the east of the Arabian Peninsula.

         lands   sea   hills

PART B.

1. Name the two important cities for Muslims on the map.

    a. _____   b. _____

2. The country in which Makkah and Madinah are located:

    _____

3. Circle the place on the map where Rasulullah ﷺ was born.

4. Circle the place on the map where Rasulullah ﷺ is buried.

Activity 3

You have read about the geography of Arabia. Look at the map of the United States and fill in the table below.

Countries	Important Cities	Important Places	Seas Oceans	Language
Saudi Arabia	malckon	mondimah	aribiah sea	arbic
United States of America	woshing Ton DC	chicago	picific	Ehglesh

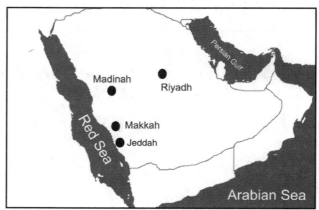

12

Activity 4

Hot is the opposite of cold. Night is the opposite of Day. Draw lines to connect the opposites.

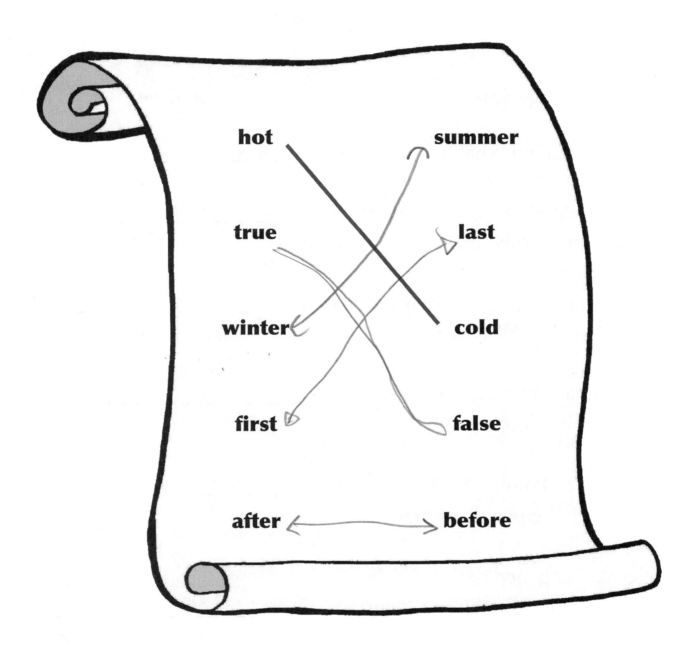

Lesson 4 — Prophet Ibrahim and Prophet Isma'il ﷺ Teach Islam

Activity 1

Pair up with one of your class mates. Take turns to pick a question and share your answer with each other for one minute.

Write the answer in the space provided.

Question	Answer
1. Who is called 'Khalilullah'?	Abrohim
2. What did Allah ﷻ tell Prophet Ibrahim ﷺ to build?	The sacred house or Kaaba
3. How did Prophet Ibrahim ﷺ feel towards Allah ﷻ?	
4. How did Allah show His love for Ibrahim ﷺ?	
5. What did Prophet Ibrahim ﷺ teach to the people of Arabia?	
6. What happened to the people after Prophet Ibrahim ﷺ died?	

Activity 2

Read lesson four again.

Number the events of the story from 1 to 5.

_____ Allah ﷻ gave Hajar and Ismail ﷺ water from the Well of Zamzam.

_____ Prophet Ibrahim ﷺ left his family alone in a valley.

_____ Some Arab tribes came to get water from the Well of Zamzam.

_____ Prophet Ibrahim ﷺ came to stay in a deserted place called Makkah.

_____ Makkah grew from a deserted place to a big city.

Activity 3

Below is a story about the Well of Zamzam.
Read the story and complete it in your own words.

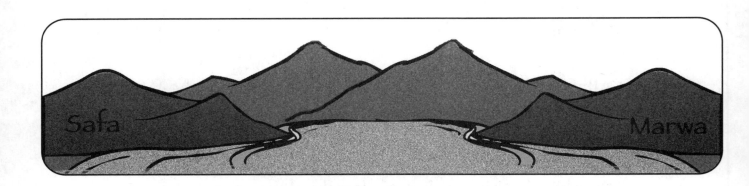

The valley was _____ and dry. Hajar 🌼 must find water for her _____.

She ran _____ times from the top of the hill of Safa across to the hill of

Marwa. There was no water anywhere. Suddenly, a miracle happened! An

angel hit the earth next to baby Ismai'l 🌼 and _____ gushed out of the

sand. She _____ the ground around the water to _____ a well. She kept

on saying, "Zam! Zam!" which meant "Stop! Stop!" Since then, the _____

is named Zamzam.

16

Activity 4

Find all the words from the box in the word search.
Use the clues below to help you.

F	E	I	S	M	E	V	A	V
R	C	S	H	A	A	J	R	A
I	S	M	A	I	L	A	B	L
G	S	G	J	C	I	A	L	L
H	V	T	A	R	T	B	L	E
T	A	Y	R	I	C	I	T	Y
E	L	A	M	S	I	G	E	T
T	T	L	A	L	Y	T	N	N
V	E	L	I	M	R	H	T	N

a. The wife of Prophet Ibrahim ﷺ.

b. A low area between two mountains.

c. The Arabs used a shelter made of cloth.

d. The son of Prophet Ibrahim ﷺ.

e. A large town.

f. The opposite of wrong.

The People of Arabia Forget Islam

Activity 1

Muslims pray only to Allah ﷻ. Only Allah is God. Besides Allah, there is no other God.

After Prophet Ibrahim ﷺ died, the people of Makkah did not believe in Allah ﷻ. How was their life?

Use the sentence starter to write your answer.

1. They believe that there were many _____.

2. Their gods were _____.

3. The idols were _____.

4. They believed in _____.

5. They placed the idols in _____.

6. The Ka'bah became _____.

Activity 2

Write in the space about how the people of Makkah behaved.

> **Prophets Ibrahim and Isma'il ﷺ taught Islam to the people of Arabia. The people forgot Allah after the death of Ibrahim ﷺ and his son.**

What did they do?

1 _____

2 _____

3 _____

4 _____

What can you say about their actions?

_____

_____

_____

Activity 3

Allah sent Rasulullah ﷺ to remind the people of Makkah to believe. Rasulullah ﷺ told us to believe in Allah ﷻ and His attributes.

Use the web to write what you believe about Allah ﷻ.

We believe that Allah ﷻ...

Activity 4

Pretend you are going to write an article about the people of Makkah. What questions will you need to ask?

Complete each question using the words in the box.

when   where   what   why

_____ did the people forget the teachings of Islam?

_____ did Allah ﷻ send Rasulullah ﷺ to the people?

_____ did Rasulullah ﷺ teach the people?

_____ did the people place the idols?

_____ did the people of Makkah worship?

Activity 1

Read the "action" in the left column. Write the "purpose" in the right column.

Action (What?)	Purpose (Why?)
People from all over Arabia came to Makkah	to visit the Ka'bah and pray to the idols.
Abraha built a big temple	
The soldiers brought the elephants across the desert	
The people of Makkah hid in the mountains	
Abdul Muttalib prayed to Allah ﷻ	
Allah ﷻ sent thousands of birds	
This year was known as the Year of the Elephant	

Activity 2

Work in a small group. See if you can identify the events that lead to the end of Abraha's army.

Start at the bottom and work your way up.

End

Allah ﷻ destroyed King Abraham and his army.

⇧

⇧

⇧

⇧

Beginning

Activity 3

Study the map below and find out more about the land of King Abraha.

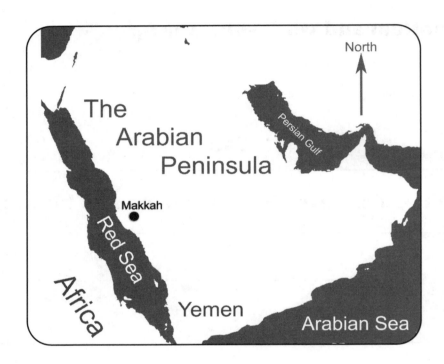

1. On the map, circle the area called Yemen.

2. Which direction is Yemen from Makkah? _____.

3. Name the two seas that touch Yemen.

   a._____   b._____

Activity 4

> Before or after tells us when an event happened. Read the story of King Abraha's attacks on the Ka'bah again to refresh your memory.

Circle before or after to tell what happens when.

1. The Ka'bah was attacked **(after, before)** Rasulullah ﷺ was born.

2. Makkah grew into a city **(after, before)** the death of Prophet Ibrahim ﷺ.

3. The people hid in the mountains **(after, before)** the army and elephants arrived in Makkah.

4. The birds attacked the soldiers **(after, before)** they arrived at the Ka'bah.

5. The people of Makkah became very happy and came down from the mountain **(after, before)** the army of Abraha was destroyed.

The Birth of Muhammad Rasulullah

Activity 1

Read the question below and write the answer on the next page.

1

Which year was Rasulullah ﷺ born?

2

What can you tell about the character of Abdullah?

3

How did Abdullah die?

4

What did Aminah dream?

5

What is the date of Muhammad's birth?

6

Who named Muhammad ﷺ?

7

What was the occupation of Abdul Muttalib?

8

Muhammad ﷺ was also called 'Ahmad' by Abdul Muttalib. Why?

9

Why was Muhammad ﷺ called a 'special baby?'

Activity 1 (CONTINUED)

Think before you answer!

1

2

3

4

5

6

7

8

9

Activity 2

Take a look at the family web of Prophet Muhammad ﷺ.

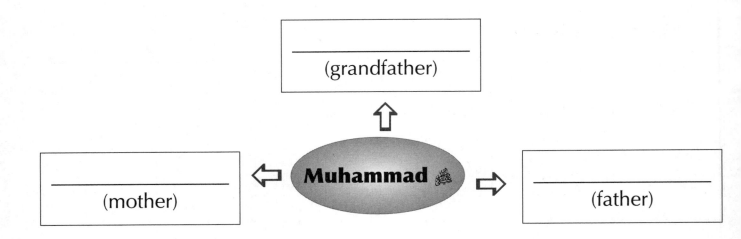

_____
(grandfather)

_____ ⬅ **Muhammad ﷺ** ➡ _____
(mother)   (father)

Draw your family web below and write their names.

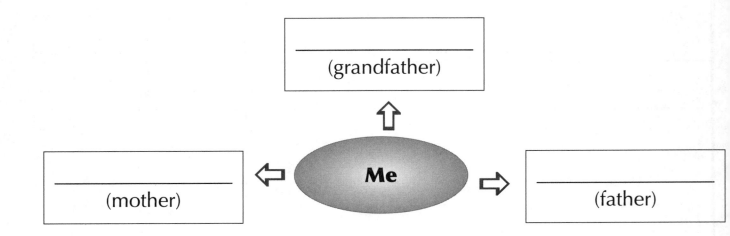

_____
(grandfather)

_____ ⬅ **Me** ➡ _____
(mother)   (father)

Activity 3

Work with one of your classmates and write a creative story about the birth of Sayyidina Muhammad ﷺ.

Use the words below.

dream	light	night	special
born	boy	happy	
Rabi al-Awwal	baby	prayed	

_____

_____

_____

_____

_____

_____

_____

_____

_____

Activity 4

There are smaller words hiding in each of these words. Can you find them? Write them on the lines.

1. i m p o r t a n t   ⇨   __or, ant, port__

2. i n t o   ⇨   _____

3. t o g e t h e r   ⇨   _____

4. s o m e t h i n g   ⇨   _____

5. m o t h e r   ⇨   _____

6. c a r e   ⇨   _____

7. e l e p h a n t   ⇨   _____

Little Muhammad ﷺ lives with Halimah رضي الله عنها

Activity 1

The sentences below tell you about little Muhammad ﷺ and his life in the countryside.

TRUE or FALSE? Write the answer on the lines.

1. The rich families of Makkah used to send their babies _____
   to live in the countryside.

2. Muhammad ﷺ was a naughty baby. _____

3. Halimah رضي الله عنها and her family were blessed with a lot of
   goods things when Muhammad ﷺ was with them. _____

4. All their plants and vegetables grew healthy and strong.

   _____

5. Muhammad ﷺ grew into a strong and healthy boy. _____

6. Muhammad ﷺ was sent back to his family after living

   with Halimah رضي الله عنها for 5 years. _____

Activity 2

Find out how life in the city of Makkah and in the village of Halimah ﷺ **were alike and how they were different.**

City of Makkah	Village of Banu Sa'd
Air	
Language	
Food	
Land	
People	

Which place would you choose to live in? Why?

_____

_____

_____

_____

Activity 3

**Read the story below about Muhammad's life with Halimah ﷺ.
Use your own words to complete the story.**

Halimah ﷺ and her husband _____ Muhammad ﷺ. When he

was young, Muhammad ﷺ helped _____ look after the sheep.

He worked together with Halimah's children. The _____

loved to work and play with him. In the _____ , Muhammad

ﷺ was loved by everyone. Every house he visited was blessed by

Allah ﷻ. The villagers were happy to have a special

_____ living with them.

Activity 4

Use the words to write creative sentences. Write your sentences on the space provided.

Nouns: young, old
Verb: jogging, walking
Adjectives: clean, fresh

_____
_____
_____
_____
_____
_____
_____

Nouns: plants, vegetables
Verb: grow, survive
Adjectives: healthy, green

_____
_____
_____
_____
_____
_____
_____

Muhammad ﷺ as a Child

Activity 1

Write what you have learned in the space below.

1. Muhammad ﷺ was an orphan. Why?

2. Muhammad ﷺ lost his mother. When?

3. Abdul Muttalib took care of Muhammad ﷺ. Why?

4. Muhammad ﷺ stayed with the noble Abu Talib. When?

5. Everyone in Makkah liked young Muhammad ﷺ. Why?

Lesson 9

Activity 2

Complete the timeline based on the story. Then write Sayyidina Muhammad's age on the lines next to A, B, and C. Answer D and it's a BONUS point for you!

Age		Events
A. _____ years old	⇨	Muhammad's father died.
B. _____ years old	⇨	Aminah ﷺ passed away.
C. _____ years old	⇨	Muhammad ﷺ lost his grandfather.
D. _____ years old	⇨	Muhammad ﷺ became a prophet.

36

Activity 3

In the following *Hadith*, Rasulullah ﷺ says:
- "The best house is the one in which orphans are well-treated."
- "The worst house is the one in which orphans are badly treated."

Think of examples that show the way we must treat orphans.

Things I will do to help children who are orphans:

_____

_____

_____

_____

_____

_____

Activity 4

Adjectives are "describing words". We use adjectives to describe people, things and places.

Prophet Muhammad ﷺ is described as *as-Sadiq* (The Truthful One) and *al-Amin* (The One You Can Trust).

Cross out the words that do not describe the Prophet ﷺ.

truthful	liar	honest
happy	friendly	angry
mean	fair	Just
helpful	kind	slow
playful	hardworking	lazy

Activity 1

1. What was the noble Abu Talib's occupation?

_____

_____

2. What did Abu Talib do as a merchant?

_____

_____

3. Where did Muhammad ﷺ go with his uncle?

_____

_____

4. Why did the people trust Muhammad ﷺ?

_____

_____

5. How do we know that the people trusted Muhammad ﷺ?

_____

_____

Activity 2

The noble Abu Talib took Muhammad ﷺ to Syria for a business trip. There they met Bahira, a Christian monk.

Work with a friend and complete the graphic organizer with the information from the lesson.

> Bahira talked to young Muhammad ﷺ.

What did Bahira tell Abu Talib about his nephew?	What did Abu Talib do?	If Muhammad ﷺ was your nephew what would you do with Bahira's advice?

What did you learn from this story?

_____

_____

Activity 3

The *Sunnah* are acts that Rasulullah ﷺ did. Allah ﷻ rewards those who follow the *Sunnah*.

Look at the pictures below. With a check, mark three *Sunnahs* that you would like to follow.

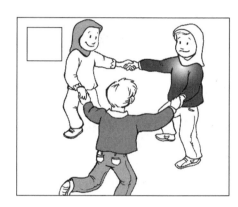

Activity 4

> A sentence has a naming part. The naming part tells us who or what the sentence is about.
>
> *For example:*
>   Muhammad's was an orphan. (Who)

<u>Underline</u> the naming part for each sentence. Write who or what on the line next to each sentence.

1. Abu Talib was a merchant. _____

2. Business is a *Sunnah*. _____

3. Traders buy and sell things. _____

4. A caravan is a group of people who travel together. _____

5. Bahira was a Christian monk. _____

6. The Injil was revealed to Prophet 'Isa ﷺ. _____

7. A scholar is clever and has lots of knowledge. _____

8. A tent is a shelter made of cloth. _____

Activity 1

Khadijah married Muhammad. Read the story again. The sentences below tell you about Makkah and Madinah.

Check the sentences below. Circle True or False.

1. Khadijah was a kind widow but she was poor. **T   F**

2. Muhammad took a caravan of goods to Syria **T   F**

3. Khadijah sent her brother to find out about Muhammad. **T   F**

4. Maisarah told Khadijah that Muhammad was fair, honest and kind. **T   F**

5. Khadijah married Muhammad because he was handsome. **T   F**

6. Muhammad married Khadijah when he was 40 years old. **T   F**

Activity 2

Write in the space to tell why Khadijah ؓ decided to marry Muhammad ﷺ.

> Khadijah ؓ was a noble lady. She was rich and beautiful. She chose to marry Muhammad ﷺ, an honest and trust worthy man.

Why did she choose to marry Muhammad ﷺ?

1. _____

2. _____

3. _____

Would you choose a good and honest person as your friend, too? Give reasons why?

_____

_____

_____

_____

_____

Activity 3

Khadijah ؓ decided to marry Muhammad ﷺ because he was fair, kind and good. Would you do the same when choosing a friend?

Use this chart to write other qualities that are important for you when choosing a friend.

A good
friend is
one who

Activity 4

A analogy is a comparison between two things which have somethings in common.

Find the similarities in the following;

1. A lady is to a gentleman;

    AS

    A girl is to a _____

    woman, boy, beautiful

2. Smile is to happy ,

    AS

    Crying is to _____

    Sadness, joy, illness

3. Grandfather is to grandmother

    AS

    Father is to _____

    Aunt, niece, mother

Activity 1

Fill in the blanks with the correct words in the brackets.

1. Muhammad ﷺ and Khadijah ؏ had _____ children.

   (three, six, one)

2. They had two sons and four _____.

   (daughters, women, girls)

3. Their sons _____ when they were very young.

   (cried, fainted, died)

4. The oldest daughter was _____ and the youngest was Fatimah ؏.

   (Zainab, Ruqayyah, Umm Kalthum)

5. Muhammad ﷺ and Khadijah ؏ taught their daughters good

   _____.

   (manners, speech, voice)

Activity 2

Prophet Muhammad's children loved and respected their parents. They obeyed them, helped them and were very kind to them.

Write some of the ways you are SIMILAR to the children of the Prophet ﷺ and some of the ways you are DIFFERENT.

Complete the table below.

	Prophet Muhammad's children	Me
Similarities	1. 2. 3. 4. 5.	1. 2. 3. 4. 5.
Differences	1. 2. 3. 4. 5.	1. 2. 3. 4. 5.

Activity 3

Khadijah رضي الله عنها and Muhammad ﷺ loved their children very much. They took good care of them. The children loved their parents.

We should follow the good manners of the children of Muhammad Rasulullah ﷺ.

Write some of the good manners which you have with your parents in the graphic organizer below.

Muslim Children Respect Their Parents

What would you do?

Dinner Time	Play Time	________ (pick your own time)
• ________ ________	• ________ ________	• ________ ________
• ________ ________	• ________ ________	• ________ ________

Activity 4

Many families like to keep a family picture. Some like to draw them.

Read the description of the family first. Draw the picture of this family with markers or crayon.

There are three children in the family. Two children are girls. The other child is a boy. The sisters wear long green dresses. The boy has short, brown and curly hair.

Activity 1

Read the action in the left column. Write the reasons in the right column.

Action (What?)	Purpose (Why?)
Khadijah ﷳ gave money to the poor	to make her husband happy.
Muhammad ﷺ and Khadijah ﷳ helped slaves	
Muhammad ﷺ went to the Cave of Hira	
Khadijah ﷳ went to the Cave of Hira	
Muhammad ﷺ stayed in the cave for many days.	

Activity 2

Allah ﷻ **told Rasulullah** ﷺ **to talk to the people of Makkah.**

Think carefully and fill in the reactions of the people of Makkah when they heard Rasulullah's message of Islam.

The People of Makkah

Did all the people of Makkah reject Rasulullah's teachings?

Activity 3

Do you know who Sayyidina Bilal ؓ was? Read the story below and unscramble the words to complete the story.

| bells Allah Bilal dream mosque roof voice adhan |

The people needed to know when it was time to come to the _____ (**o s q u e m**) to pray. Some said to use _____ (**e l l s b**) like in a church. Others said to have horns or drums. Rasulullah ﷺ disagreed.

A man came to Rasulullah ﷺ and told him about a _____ (**e a r m d**) he had. He dreamt a person with a beautiful voice was calling out phrases in a loud voice. Rasulullah ﷺ knew the dream was from _____ (**l l a h A**).

A beloved Sahabi of Rasulullah ﷺ, named _____ (**i l l a b**) had a beautiful voice. Rasulullah ﷺ told the man who had the dream teach the words to Bilal ؓ. Then Bilal ؓ went up to the _____ (**orof**) of the mosque and called out the words loudly with his beautiful voice.

When the Muslims heard Bilal's _____ (**e c i o v**) they came running to the _____ (**m q o u s e**) to pray. Bilal ؓ became the first Mu'adhin because he made the first _____ (**d h a n**).

Activity 4

Find all the words from the box in the word search. Use the clues below to help you.

```
H   K   T   S   A   F   M   G
I   D   H   L   T   O   A   P
M   H   I   R   A   S   K   H
K   C   N   S   V   E   K   S
O   V   K   L   T   H   A   E
A   A   M   A   K   N   H   K
I   L   H   I   R   T   M   T
I   D   O   L   S   S   D   O
R   A   N   J   H   I   O   P
```

1. The name of the cave Muhammad ﷺ stayed is <u>Hira</u>.

2. The cave is at the <u>top</u> of the mountain.

3. Cave Hira is in the mountain near <u>Makkah</u>.

4. Muhammad ﷺ stayed in the cave to <u>think</u>.

5. Muhammad ﷺ did not believe in the <u>idols</u>.

Angel Jibril As Visits Muhammad ﷺ

Activity 1

Read the questions below and write your answers in the empty boxes below.

1	2	3
Who was the angel that came to see Muhammad ﷺ?	What happened on the night Muhammad ﷺ was in the Cave of Hira?	How did Muhammad ﷺ feel when he saw Jibril ؏?

4	5	6
What did Angel Jibril ؏ tell Muhammad ﷺ to do?	Why didn't Muhammad ﷺ read when told to by Angel Jibril ؏?	Which *Surah* did Angel Jibril ؏ read to Muhammad ﷺ?

1	2	3

4	5	6

Activity 2

When we quote someone's words in our writing we always write these words between inverted commas like this: "   ". These are called <u>quotation marks</u>.

Complete the organizer below with the exact words of Angel Jibril and Prophet Muhammad using quotation marks.

Angel Jibril said:

"Read!"

⇩

Muhammad said:

⇩

Angel Jibril said:

⇩

Muhammad said:

Angel Jibril read verses 1 to 5 of *Surah al-Alaq* to Prophet Muhammad.

Activity 3

The first verse Angel Jibril ﷻ brought to Prophet Muhammad ﷺ was "Read!"

Draw or paste pictures to show the books that you like to read.

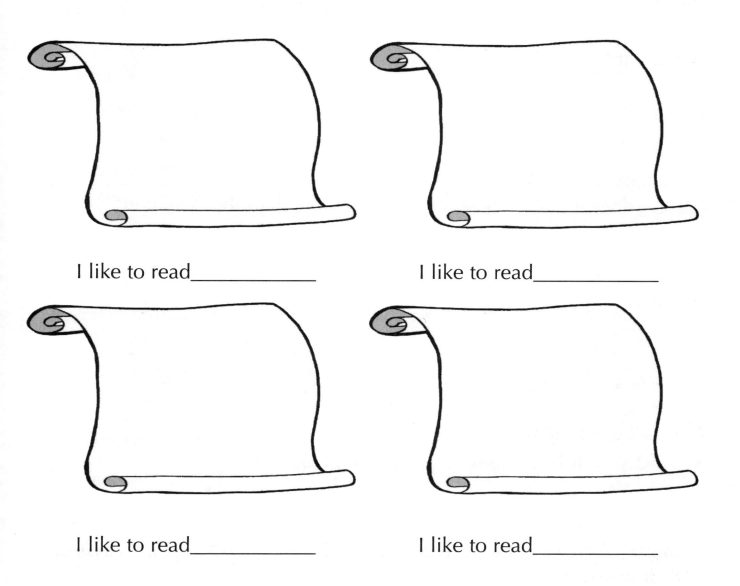

I like to read_____

I like to read_____

I like to read_____

I like to read_____

Activity 4

Read a book and fill in the information using the table below. Share your report with your class.

Title_____   Author _____

What or who is the story about?	Where does this story take place?

How does this story begin?	How does the story end?

List five words from this story that are new to you.

Would you tell a friend to read this book? Why?

_____

_____

Khadijah Comforts Muhammad

Activity 1

Read each quotation below. Can you recall who said it? Why did the person say it?

Write your answer in the space provided.

"Muhammad! You are Allah's Messenger and I am Jibril."

Who said this?	
Why was it said?	

"I am afraid. I have seen such a strange thing."

Who said this?	
Why was it said?	

Activity 2

Khadijah ؓ comforted Rasulullah ﷺ. What did she say?
Waraqah advised Rasulullah ﷺ. What did he say?

When we write someone's words we put them in between the inverted commas like " ."

Khadijah ؓ

Quote the words of Khadijah ؓ below
"   "

Waraqah

Quote Waraqah's answer to Rasulullah ﷺ
"   "

Who was Waraqah?

_____

_____

Activity 3

Prophet Muhammad ﷺ was scared. Khadijah ؓ comforted him. What did she say to him?

> **"Don't be afraid. You are an honest and truthful man. You are kind to everyone. You help the poor. Allah loves people like you. He will take care of you."**

Now what would you say if...

Your brother lost his toy. He is sad.

Your mother is sick. She needs you to help her.

Activity 4

- • Remember, we put quotation marks around words that people are saying.
- • For example: "Cover me up! Cover me up!"

Write three sentences that show you saying something. Practice writing quotation marks around them.

1.

2.

3.

Muhammad ﷺ Becomes Rasulullah ﷺ

Lesson 16

Activity 1

Prophet Muhammad ﷺ is Allah's messenger. The sentences below tell you what Angel Jibril عليه السلام told Rasulullah ﷺ.

Check the sentences, then circle <u>Yes</u> or <u>No</u>.

1. Angel Jibril عليه السلام brought messages from Allah سبحانه وتعالى to Rasulullah ﷺ.   Y   N

2. Muhammad ﷺ was chosen to be Allah's Messenger   Y   N

3. Allah told Rasulullah ﷺ to teach Islam to his family.   Y   N

4. Jibril عليه السلام taught Muhammad ﷺ about Allah سبحانه وتعالى.   Y   N

5. Those who follow his teachings are believers.   Y   N

6. The *Kuffar* of Makkah agreed to follow Rasulullah's teachings.   Y   N

Activity 2

Muhammad ﷺ is Allah's messenger. What does Allah ﷻ want a messenger to do?

Write the things Muhammad ﷺ had to do when Allah ﷻ made him a prophet.

Muhammad ﷺ becomes a prophet. ⟹

Activity 3

Allah ﷾ told Rasulullah ﷺ to teach Islam to the people.
Rasulullah ﷺ learned the Qur'an. What other things did he do?

We, too, must teach Islam to others.

Write three things we can do to teach Islam to others.

1.

2.

3.

Lesson 16

Activity 4

"O Allah! I will do what you want me to do. I will teach the people about Islam"

Your teacher has asked you to deliver a short talk about Allah ﷻ to your class.

Write your talk in the box below. Present it to your class.

There is only One God…

Activity 1

Work with a friend. Take turns picking a question. Figure out the answers together.

Write the answer in the space provided.

Question	Answer
1. Who are the first people Rasulullah ﷺ talked to about Islam?	
2. Who was the first lady to accept Islam?	
3. Who was Rasulullah's first friend to believe in him?	
4. Who was the first youth to accept Islam?	
5. Who was the first slave to accept Islam?	

Activity 2

Write about what made the first believers accept Rasulullah's message.

> **Many people who knew Rasulullah ﷺ believed in him. They accepted Islam and became Muslims.**

Why did they believe in Rasulullah ﷺ?

Khadijah ﷺ _____

Abu Bakr ﷺ _____

Ali ﷺ _____

Zaid ﷺ _____

Any Muslim who saw Rasulullah ﷺ is called a *Sahabi*.

What do we say when we hear the name of a *Sahabi*?

_____

_____

Activity 3

The first four *Sahabah* of Rasulullah ﷺ had great trust in him. This trust helped them to accept his words and believe that he was the last prophet sent by Allah ﷻ.

Let us read the poem called TRUST by Jay Narain and think what Rasulullah ﷺ had done to win the trust of his *Sahabah*.

What is trust?
Ask no question.
Believe in someone's all the words and actions.
How to get entrusted?
Start a little uphill journey,
Don't deceive or take someone's dreams,
Don't lie or take advantage of someone.
Trust is blind faith,
Don't stab its back.

What are some of the actions you will take in order to win the trust of your friends and family members?

1. _____

2. _____

3. _____

Activity 4

An antonym means the opposite of a word. Write the opposite of each of the words below.

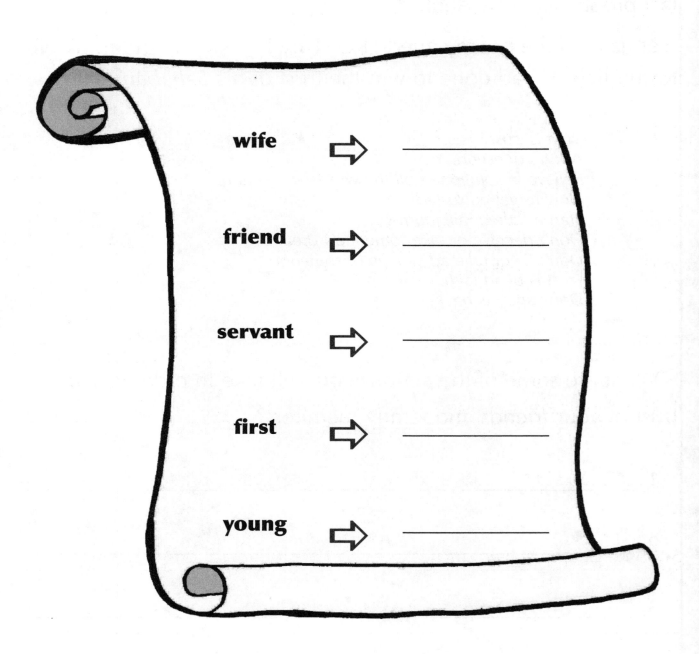

wife   ⇨ _____

friend   ⇨ _____

servant   ⇨ _____

first   ⇨ _____

young   ⇨ _____

Rasulullah ﷺ Invites the People of Makkah

Activity 1

Write what you have learned in the space below.

1. Rasulullah ﷺ climbed the Hill of Safa. Why?

2. Rasulullah ﷺ told the people there was great danger. Why?

3. The people of Makkah were angry. Why?

4. The people did not listen to Rasulullah ﷺ. Why?

5. Some people stayed and listened to Rasulullah ﷺ. Why?

Activity 2

Allah ﷻ told Rasulullah ﷺ to talk to the people of Makkah. How did these people react to him?

Fill in the Makkans' reactions in the chart below.

The People of Makkah

Did all the Makkans' reject Rasulullah's teachings?

Activity 3

Do you know who Abu Lahab was? Read the story below.

Abu Lahab was an uncle of Rasulullah ﷺ. His real name was Abdul 'Uzza bin Abdul Muttalib. He did not listen to Rasulullah ﷺ. He called Rasulullah ﷺ a liar. His wife was not a nice woman. She did not like Rasulullah ﷺ either. She threw stones at Rasulullah ﷺ and called him crazy. Abu Lahab and his wife were great enemies of Prophet Muhammad ﷺ. Allah ﷻ talks about Abu Lahab and his wife in Surah al-Lahab.

As you read the passage, think of the following questions:

a. Who was the father of Abu Lahab?

_____

_____

b. Abu Talib was the brother of Abu Lahab. Think and write about how Abu Talib treated Prophet Muhammad ﷺ.

_____

_____

Activity 4

There are smaller words hiding in each of these words. Can you find them? Write them in the boxes

1. m e s s a g e   ⇨   **Mess, sage, gas, age**

2. c l a s s m a t e   ⇨   _____

3. c l i m b e d   ⇨   _____

4. d a n g e r   ⇨   _____

5. t r u s t   ⇨   _____

6. p r a y   ⇨   _____

7. l i s t e n   ⇨   _____

The Muslims and the Kuffar

Activity 1

Who were the *Sahabah* ?

Think about some of the activities which *Sahabah* would have done in a day. Make a list in the table below with your friends.

1.

2.

3.

4.

5.

Activity 2

Rasulullah ﷺ taught Islam to everyone. Some became Muslims. Others did not. They became the *Kuffar*. Find out how they were different from the *Sahabah* رضي الله عنهم?

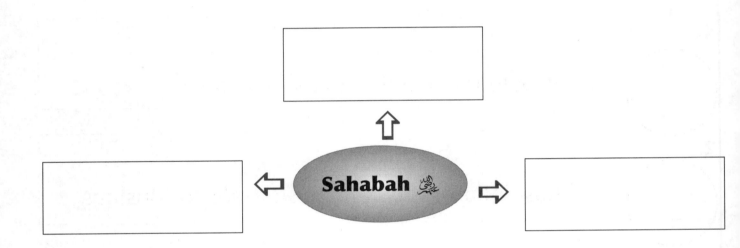

HOW THEY WERE DIFFERENT?

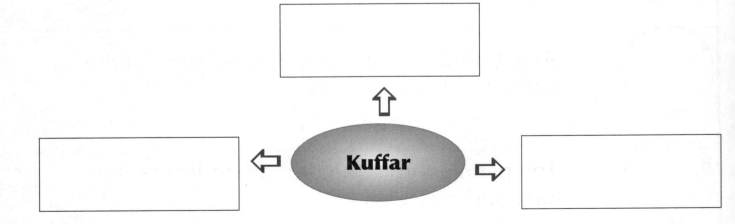

Activity 3- Once Upon a Time

Be a historian and tell the story of the Qur'an by rearranging the sentences in the correct order.

Write the number in the circle.

◯ People learned the *ayahs* by heart.

◯ Rasulullah ﷺ recited those *ayahs* to Muslims.

◯ The whole Qur'an was revealed over 23 years.

◯ Angel Jibril ﷽ came and recited parts of the Qur'an to Rasulullah ﷺ.

◯ The people wrote the Qur'an on leaves, tree bark and clay plates.

Activity 4

Adjectives are describing words. We use adjectives to describe people, things and places.

Color the words that describe the *Kuffar* of Makkah.

Muslims	stubborn	images
Truthful	angry	disbelievers
Sahabah ﷺ	Did not like Rasulullah ﷺ	arrogant

The Kuffar Persecute the Muslims

Activity 1

Fill in the blanks with the correct words in the brackets.

1. The *Kuffar* of Makkah told Rasulullah ﷺ to _____ teaching Islam.

   (stop, pause, continue)

2. Rasulullah ﷺ was _____ when the *Kuffar* of Makkah made fun of him.

   (sad, patient, annoyed)

3. Some of the *Kuffar* threw _____ on Rasulullah ﷺ.

   (boxes, flowers, garbage)

4. The *Kuffar* of Makkah _____ the Muslims.

   (fed, hurt, helped)

5. The Christian king _____ the Muslims from the *Kuffar* of Makkah.

   (protected, harmed , caught)

6. The Muslims were _____ and their faith was strong.

   (patient, scared, braved)

Lesson 20

Activity 2

Most of the *Kuffar* of Makkah were rich and strong. The *Sahabah* ﷺ were weak and poor. The *Kuffar* became Rasulullah's enemies.

Describe and resolve the problem the *Sahabah* ﷺ faced with the *Kuffar* of Makkah. Think and write how Rasulullah ﷺ solved the problem.

The Problem?
The *Kuffar* of Makkah persecuted the poor and helpless Muslims.

Describe some of the ways Muslims were persecuted.

1. _____

2. _____

3. _____

4. _____

The Solution

_____

_____

80

Activity 3

Study the map. Complete the sentence with the correct answer.

Africa

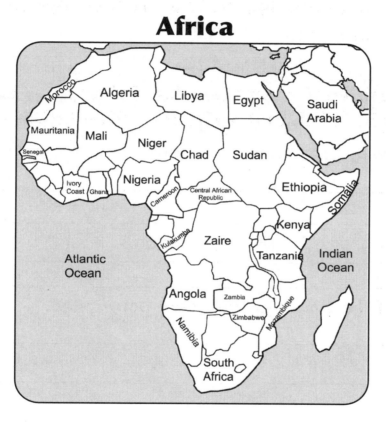

1. The Muslims left for _____ to escape the *Kuffar* of Makkah.

2. Prophet Muhammad ﷺ said that the _____ was a good man.

3. The king was a _____.

4. Look at the map. The land called Ethiopia is located on the continent of _____.

5. On the map, color the land called Ethiopia.

Lesson 20

Activity 4

Adjectives are describing words. Verbs are action words. Write each word from the word box in the correct group.

weak   poor   helpless   rich
strong   hot   brave   good   move   lie
sit   threw   kill   laugh   talk
walk   throw   help   happy

Verbs (Action Words)

Adjectives (Describing words)

Activity 1

Read the action in the left column. Write the reasons in the right column.

Action (What?)	Purpose (Why?)
1. The Muslims left for Ethiopia	to ..
2. *Hijrah* means	
3. A group of the *Kuffar* went to Ethiopia	
4. The *Sahabi* Jafar ﷺ spoke to the king.	
5. The Muslims were happy	

Activity 2

Find out how Abu Lahab and King Najashi were alike and how they were different. Talk with your classmates for ideas!

Abu Lahab   **King Najashi**

How were they the same?

_____

_____

_____

How were they different?

Religion
_____

Rank
_____

Place
_____

How do you feel about both of them? Why?

_____

_____

_____

Activity 3

King Najashi had mercy on the Muslims. He protected them from harm.

The Prophet Muhammad ﷺ once said:

> **"Allah will not be merciful to those who are not merciful."**
>
> (al-Bukhari)

List the things we can do to show mercy to others.

1. _____

2. _____

3. _____

4. _____

Activity 4

Before or after tells us when an event happened. Read the story of the Muslims and King Najashi

Circle before or after to tell what happens when.

1. A group of Muslim left for Ethiopia (**after, before**) the *Kuffar* of Makkah began to persecute them.

2. The Muslims left Makkah (**after, before**) the *Kuffar* found out that they were missing.

3. Some *Kuffar* went to see King Najashi (**after, before**) they found out that a group of Muslims had left for Ethiopia.

4. Ja'far ؊ spoke about Islam (**after, before**) King Najashi met the *Kuffar* of Makkah.

5. King Najashi told the *Kuffar* to go home (**after, before**) listening to Ja'far ؊ talk about Islam.

The Teachings of Islam

Activity 1

A. **Read the poem in the "Tune In" section of your text book lesson 22.**

> Related to none,
> Allah is One!
> Equal to none.
> No mother, no father,
> No daughter or son,
> Allah is One!

Circle the quality of Allah ﷻ above poem talks about.

Tawhid   Al-Qadr   Al-Khaliq

B. **Read the following poem and circle the quality of Allah ﷻ this one talks about.**

> I am a Muslim and Allah made me,
> He made my family and He made me.
> He made the sun and the moon
> He made all animals and the beautiful birds.
> Allah made everything and everyone
> I am a Muslim and Allah made me.

Ar-Rahman   Al-Khaliq   Ar-Rahim

Lesson 22

Activity 2

Fill in the circles below with the teachings of Rasulullah ﷺ about Allah ﷻ and about the idols.

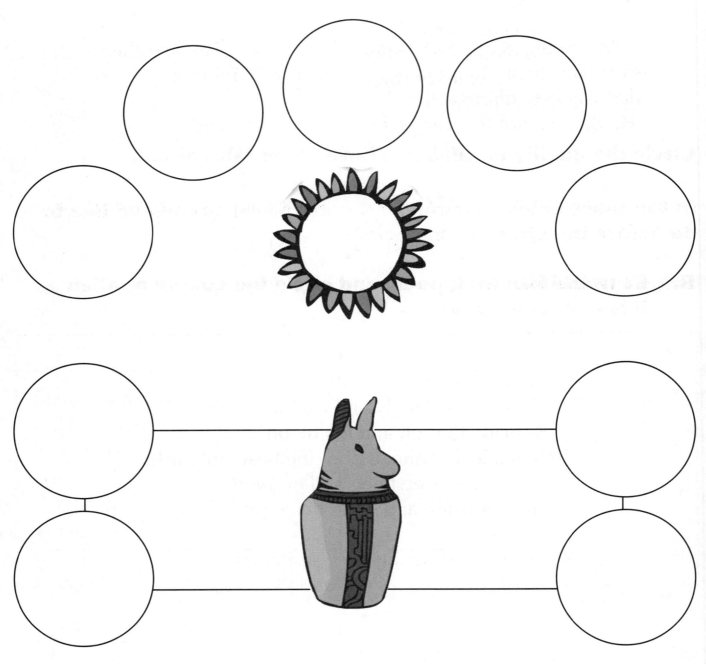

Activity 3

Rasulullah ﷺ taught the Qur'an to the believers. He taught them about the *Qiyamah*. What did Rasulullah ﷺ say about the *Qiyamah*?

> **"When the sky will break and the stars will fall, and the earth will shake, and the mountains will fly into pieces...on that day everything will end."**
> He then taught the people how to do good deeds

In the space below, list down all good deeds you would like to do before the *Qiyamah* happens!

Thing I would like to do....

1. _____

2. _____

3. _____

4. _____

Activity 4

| hood | hay | ball |
| fly | hair | |

Use the words from the box to answer the questions.

1. Write the word which rhymes which wood? _____.

2. Write the word which rhymes with sky? _____.

3. Write the word which rhymes with fall? _____.

4. Write the word which rhymes with day? _____.

5. Write the word which rhymes with fair? _____.

Activity 1

Read and put a check in the box next to the correct sentences.

1. The *Kuffar* of Makkah were angry because--
   ▲ Many people accepted Islam.
   ▲ Many people refused Islam.

2. They wanted Rasulullah ﷺ to stop teaching Islam.
   ▲ They tried to bribe Rasulullah ﷺ.
   ▲ They tried to kill Rasulullah ﷺ.

3. Rasulullah ﷺ did not accept their offer.
   ▲ They offered Rasulullah ﷺ a car.
   ▲ They asked Rasulullah ﷺ to be their king.

4. Rasulullah ﷺ said…
   ▲ I am a famous person in Makkah.
   ▲ I am Allah's Prophet and Messenger.

5. The *Kuffar* could not stop Rasulullah ﷺ from teaching Islam.
   ▲ They accepted Islam.
   ▲ They became very angry.

The Kuffar Try to Bribe Rasulullah

Activity 2

The *Kuffar* of Makkah tried to stop the spread of Islam. They made Rasulullah ﷺ an offer.

Let's find out Rasulullah's answer to the Kuffar. Complete the table below.

What is the Problem?
The *Kuffar* tried to bribe Rasulullah ﷺ. They wanted him to stop teaching Islam.

What did the *Kuffar* offer Rasulullah ﷺ?
1. _____
2. _____
3. _____

What did Rasulullah ﷺ say?
_____

What is the moral of the story?

_____

_____

Activity 3

The Story of Abu Talib

Do you remember Abu Talib, the Prophet's uncle? Read the story below and complete it by using the words in the box.

> Islam   stop   right   moon   death

The *Kuffar* went to Abu Talib. They told him to stop his nephew, Muhammad ﷺ, from spreading _____. Then Abu Talib went to Rasulullah ﷺ. He told his nephew to save himself. He told him to _____ his work. Rasulullah ﷺ replied to his uncle, "If they put the sun in my _____ hand and the _____ in my left hand, I will never stop my work. I would not stop until my work is complete or _____ has come to me."

Activity 4

Color the Hidden Words

Find all the words from the box in the word search. Use the clues below to help you.

D	I	R	B	N	K	I	Y	E
T	D	F	B	R	I	B	E	H
Y	O	J	H	G	N	O	L	K
I	L	A	I	S	G	D	L	I
S	S	P	L	A	K	F	A	N
L	S	L	B	A	L	L	A	H
A	L	L	H	M	K	I	O	N
M	C	B	R	R	E	H	S	E
C	S	I	M	O	N	E	Y	Y

1. The *Kuffar* tried to <u>bribe</u> Rasulullah ﷺ.

2. The *Kuffar* wanted Rasulullah ﷺ to stop the spread of <u>Islam</u>

3. They asked Rasulullah ﷺ to be the <u>king</u>.

4. Rasulullah ﷺ refused their <u>money</u>.

5. Rasulullah ﷺ told the *Kuffar* to believe in <u>Allah</u> ﷻ.

6. The *Kuffar* believed in <u>idols</u>.

More and More People Accept Islam

Activity 1

Islam was growing in Makkah. Read the lesson's story. The sentences explain how Islam spread.

Read the sentences below. Circle Yes or No.

1. People outside Makkah came to learn the Qur'an.   Y   N

2. Abu Dharr ؓ from the tribe of Ghiffar   Y   N
   accepted Islam

3. Hamza ؓ accepted Islam as he was happy   Y   N
   with Rasulullah ﷺ.

4. Umar ؓ who was a great enemy of Islam   Y   N
   at first, did not accept Islam.

5. The *Kuffar* of Makkah stopped talking to the Muslims.   Y   N

Activity 2

Many Makkans accepted Islam. The *Kuffar* became worried.

Write some of the ways the *Kuffar* of Makkah treated the Muslims.

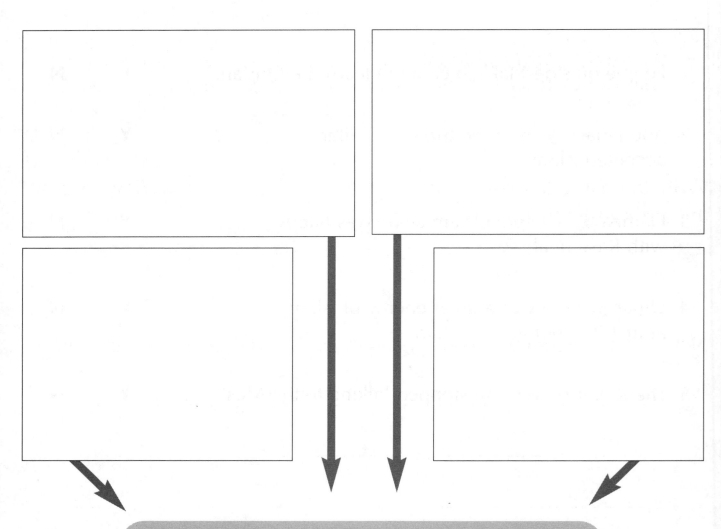

The Kuffar treated the Muslims unkindly.

Activity 3

Rasulullah ﷺ is the most beloved person Allah made. Allah ﷻ protected him and listened to his *Du'as*. Read the following *Du'a* of Rasulullah ﷺ. How did Allah ﷻ answer it?

> "O Allah! Help the Muslims by making one of these two men believe: 'Umar ibn al-Khattab or Abu Jahl ibn Hisham."

Write the name of the person who accepted Islam and became one of the strongest Muslims of all times:

_____

Now write in your own words the story of 'Umar's acceptance of Islam:

_____

_____

_____

Activity 4

Choose the odd one out in each line. Write its first letter in the space.

Salah ⇨ Statue ⇨ Idols ⇨ **S**

Angry ⇨ Night ⇨ Day ⇨

Hamza ⇨ Abu Lahab ⇨ Abu Jahal ⇨

Muslims ⇨ Arabia ⇨ Kuffar ⇨

Qur'an ⇨ Bible ⇨ Hadith ⇨

Makkah ⇨ Madinah ⇨ India ⇨

When you're done, the letters will spell a word. Can you guess it?

—— —— —— —— ——

The Boycott

Activity 1

Imagine a hot barren valley outside Makkah and fill in the words which tell you about each category below:

CLIMATE: (write words which tell about the climate of the valley of Abi Talib)

FOOD AND DRINK: (Think the kind of food items were available to the Muslims in the valley for three years)

SHELTER: (places they lived and Slept, cooked their food etc.)

WORK AND BUSINESS: (how did people have earned their living?)

Write a brief description of the conditions in which Rasulullah ﷺ, his family and the believers lived during their three years in the valley.

_____

_____

_____

Activity 2

Read the lesson again. Write in the space the things Khadijah ﷺ and the noble Abu Talib did for Rasulullah ﷺ when they were alive.

> **Khadijah ﷺ and Abu Talib were special people. They did many things for Rasulullah ﷺ.**

Khadijah ﷺ

_____

_____

_____

Abu Talib

_____

_____

_____

What will I do for Rasulullah ﷺ?

_____

_____

_____

Activity 3

When Abu Talib and Khadijah ☺ died, Rasulullah ☺ was sad. He said:

> **"It was their time to leave this world. Allah gives us life and He makes us die. All of us will die one day. Only Allah lasts forever. Only He is eternal and has no end."**

Now what would you say if...

Your sister's pet bird just died. Your sister is upset. What would you say to her?

Your uncle's favorite rose bush died. He is sad. What would you say to him?

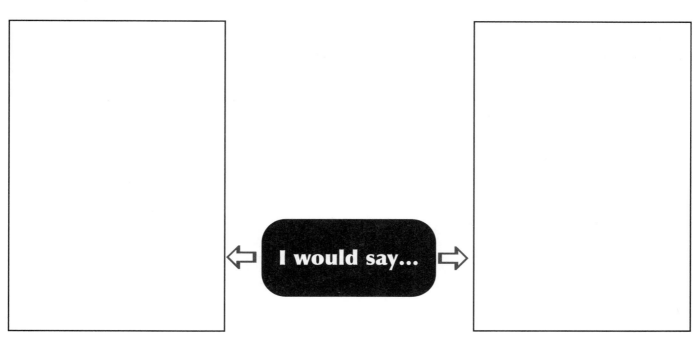

I would say...

Lesson 25

Activity 4

There are smaller words hiding in each of the words below. Can you find them? Write them on the lines.

1. b o y c o t t   ⇨   **cot, boy** _____

2. y e a r s   ⇨   _____

3. l i s t e n   ⇨   _____

4. k u f f a r   ⇨   _____

5. c a r e   ⇨   _____

The People of Taif

Activity 1

Read and complete the sentences. Check the correct sentences in the box.

1. The people of Ta'if did not believe in Allah ﷻ. Instead...
   - ▲ they believed in Rasulullah ﷺ.
   - ▲ they believed in idols.

2. Rasulullah ﷺ told them about the ...
   - ▲ teachings of the gods.
   - ▲ teachings of Islam.

3. The people of Ta'if did not accept Islam...
   - ▲ and were happy listening to the words of the Qur'an
   - ▲ and disliked hearing the words of the Qur'an.

4. The children threw rocks at Rasulullah ﷺ...
   - ▲ and the people called him crazy.
   - ▲ and the people called him a hero.

5. Rasulullah ﷺ was chased out of town...
   - ▲ but he was not angry. He asked Allah ﷻ to guide the people.
   - ▲ but he was angry. He asked Allah ﷻ to destroy the people.

Activity 2

The people of Ta'if were mean to Rasulullah ﷺ. But he was not angry with them.

Write about Rasulullah's response to the actions of the people of Ta'if.

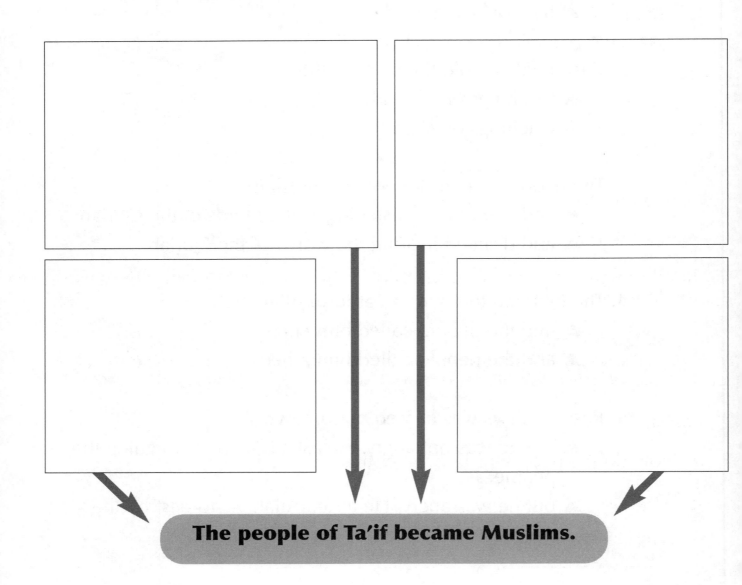

The people of Ta'if became Muslims.

Activity 3

Study the map below. Can you find the town of Ta'if?

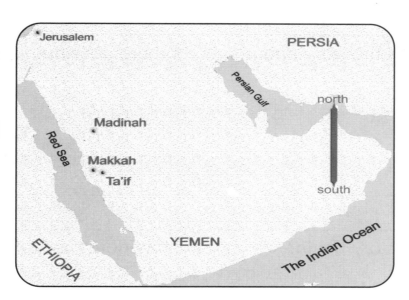

Map of Arabia

1. Name the Peninsula where Ta'if is located. _____.

2. Name the direction of the town Ta'if from Makkah. _____.

3. Read these special physical features of the town of Ta'if and then answer the following questions.

> *Ta'if had many beautiful orchards and farms. Ta'if got plenty of rain. People of Ta'if were farmers and shepherds. The climate of Ta'if is cooler than that of Makkah. In the winter it gets very cold.*

Questions:

A. How do the people of Ta'if water their orchards? _____

B. What do the shepherds of Ta'if feed their animals? _____

C. Why do the people of Makkah like to spend their summer in Ta'if?

_____

Activity 4

Fill in the information using the table below.

What or who is the story about?	Where does this story take place?

How does this story begin?	How does the story end?

List five words from the story that are new to you.

How do you feel about the ending of the story?

_____

_____

Isra' and Mi'raj

Activity 1

Prophet Muhammad ﷺ traveled from Masjid al-Aqsa to the Heavens. This journey is called the *Mi'raj*. Many things happened to Rasulullah ﷺ on this trip. What were those things?

Fill in the information for each topic in the box.

> *Jannah*

> *Jahannam*

What happened to Rasulullah ﷺ?

> *Siradrat ul-Muntaha*

> *Salah*

What made the people happy about the *Isra'* and *Mi'raj*?

Activity 2

Read the question below and share your answers with the class.

Write your answers on the next page.

1

What was the night journey of Rasulullah ﷺ called?

2

Why was Rasulullah ﷺ invited for this night journey?

3

Who invited Rasulullah ﷺ?

4

What is Rasulullah's journey from Makkah to al-Quds called?

5

Who did Allah sent to accompany Rasulullah ﷺ to Heaven?

6

What did Rasulullah ﷺ ride on?

7

Where is Masjid al-Aqsa?

8

What did Rasulullah ﷺ do in Masjid al-Aqsa?

9

Who did Rasulullah ﷺ pray with in Masjid al-Aqsa?

Activity 2 – continued

Think before you answer!

1

2

3

4

5

6

7

8

9

Activity 3

Study the map below. Then complete the activities below.

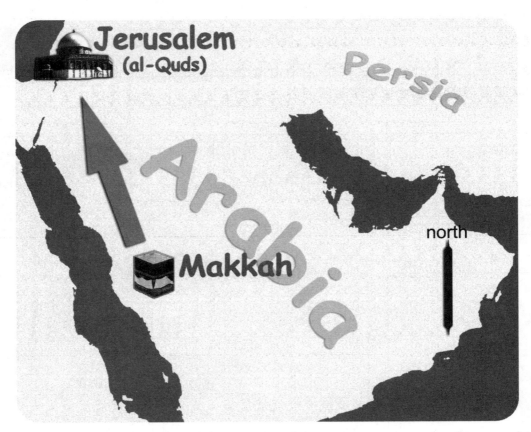

1. Al-Quds is the name in Arabic for _____.

2. Circle Jerusalam on the map.

3. How far is Jerusalam from Makkah? _____.

4. What is the direction of Makkah from Jerusalam? _____.

Activity 4

Rasulullah ﷺ rode on a Buraq. A Buraq was a creature with wings that traveled faster than light.

If you can choose your own Buraq, how would it look? In the space below, draw a picture of your Buraq. Then write a short paragraph describing it.

A Picture of My Buraq

My Buraq will

_____

_____

_____

_____

Lesson 28 — The People of Madinah Accept Islam

Activity 1-A

Look at the three holiest *masajid* for Muslims. Write the name of the city each one of them is located next to the picture.

_____   _____   _____

Activity 1 - B

Question	Answer
1. What is the meaning of *Ansar*?	
2. Who is called *Ansar*?	
3. Where did the *Ansar* come from?	
4. Why did they come to Makkah?	
5. What did Rasulullah ﷺ teach them?	

Activity 2

With three or four classmates, write down everything you can think of about the Ansar of Madinah.

al-Ansar (the Helpers)

1. City the *Ansar* came from.

   _____

2. Lcation of their city.

   _____

3. Reason for their visit to Ka'bah.

   _____

4. What did Rasulullah ﷺ told them about Islam?

   _____

5. Their answers to Rasulullah ﷺ.

   _____

6. Rasulullah called them. _____

   _____

7. Any thing else you know about the *Ansar*.

   _____

<u>Read Lesson 28 of your textbook to find the above information.</u>

Write a group report of your discussion about *Ansar* in a separate sheet of paper.

Activity 3

This is a map of the city of Madinah as it is today. Look at the map keys below. Then color the map to match the map keys.

Map of Madinah

Map Key:

Date Orchards = Green   Route = black

Houses = Yellow & white   Masjid un-Nabi = Green

Market = any colors or colors you like

Activity 4

Read the following sentences. Then place the words of the *Ansar* ﷺ and Rasulullah ﷺ in quotation marks. At the bottom of each quotation, give name of the person or persons whose words are quoted.

Obey Allah ﷻ and do good actions.

_____

You are now Allah's *Ansar* (His Helpers).

_____

We are Muslims. We will be Allah's *Ansar*.

_____

Lesson
28

Activity 1

Fill in the blanks with the correct words in the brackets.

1. Rasulullah ﷺ was known in Makkah as the most _____ person.

(trusted, dishonest, harmful)

2. The people of Makkah would go to Rasulullah ﷺ to _____ their arguments.

(accept, settle , offer)

3. Prophet Muhammad ﷺ was a _____ and just man.

(fair, unfair, liar)

4. People were always _____with his decisions.

(unhappy, happy, upset)

5. Rasulullah ﷺ always made the people work _____.

(together, separately, alone)

6. Prophet Muhammad ﷺ did not like _____and wanted everyone to live in peace.

(disputes, harmony, unity)

116

Activity 2

Once the Ka'bah was damaged by rain. The tribes of Quraish worked and repaired the Ka'bah. After the work was completed the men began to argue over who would place the famous Black Stone back into the wall of the Ka'bah.

Describe how Rasulullah ﷺ solved this argument?

1. _____

2. _____

3. _____

4. _____

Why was this such a good idea?

_____

_____

_____

_____

Activity 3

Rasulullah ﷺ made the leaders work together to solve the problem of the Black Stone.

Work with your class to raise funds for one of the following projects:

A. Visit a home for the elderly and share your art with them.
B. Raise funds for a food depository in your town.
C. Plant trees around your school on Earth Day.
D. Any other service in which you work together as a group.

Write about your plan. Tell why you want to do it

_____

_____

_____

_____

Activity 4

Prophet Muhammad ﷺ was described as peacemaker. What are some other qualities of Rasulullah ﷺ that we should know?

Circle the words that describe Prophet Muhammad ﷺ.

Honest	truthful	liar
just	wise	old
fair	peaceful	clever
problem solver	kind	loving
helpful	co-operative	lazy

Activity 1

Check the sentences below. Circle Yes or No.

1. Rasulullah always forgave and prayed for his enemies. Y N

2. Those who hurt him were punished. Y N

3. His daughter always worried about Rasulullah ﷺ. Y N

4. Rasulullah ﷺ told us that Allah ﷻ always protects those who work for Him. Y N

5. His enemies never accepted Islam because Rasulullah ﷺ was too kind. Y N

Activity 2

Rasulullah ﷺ was loving and kind to everyone he met.

List four examples of Rasulullah's compassion and kindness. Then write about one.

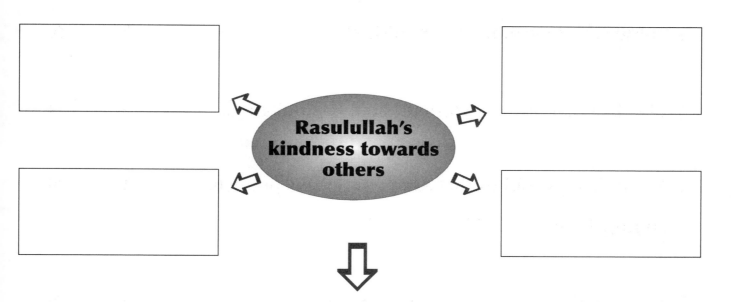

Rasulullah's kindness towards others

The effects of Rasulullah's compassion and kindness to his enemies

Activity 3

Rasulullah ﷺ taught us to be kind and compassionate to others. We must show compassion to others.

Write three things you can do to show compassion to others.

1. Family Members

2. Friends

3. Animals

Activity 4

Synonyms are words with the same or almost the same meaning. Use the words in the oval to find the word which has the same meaning.

caring   hurt   shout   furious   peaceful

kind   _____

harm   _____

yell   _____

angry   _____

calm   _____

Activity 1

Rasulullah ﷺ was known as *al-Amin*. Why?

Use the sentence starter to write your answer. Choose the correct words in the box.

| promises   example   lied   *Sunnah*   trust |

1. *Al-Amin* is a title of Rasulullah's, which means a person you can

   _____.

2. Rasulullah ﷺ always kept his word and _____.

3. We must follow Rasulullah's _____ and keep our promises.

4. The people of Makkah believed Rasulullah ﷺ because he never

   _____.

5. Keeping promises is a _____.

Activity 2

Read Lesson 31 one more time.

Write in the space to show how Rasulullah ﷺ kept his promises.

> **Rasulullah ﷺ promised 'Abdullah to meet him at a place.**

What happened?

_____

_____

_____

_____

Would you do as Rasulullah ﷺ did?

_____

_____

Activity 3

This story shows how Rasulullah ﷺ kept his promises.
List four reasons why it is important to keep promises.

1.

2.

3.

4.

Activity 4

Pick a scene to act out with a classmate. Discuss what happens when we don't keep our promises.

Fahad borrowed Lutfi's book and promised to return it to him the next day. Fahad did not return the book. Lutfi was punished by his teacher.

Nadira promised to meet Sarah after school at the library. Nadira did not turn up. Sarah missed her bus.

Kashan promised to baby-sit his younger brother. His mother had to buy the groceries for dinner. Kashan joined his friends to play football. His family had no dinner that night.

The Teachings of Our Prophet

Activity 1

The sentences below tell you about Makkah and Madinah.

Are they TRUE or FALSE? Circle True or False.

1. The teachings of the Qur'an are for everyone.   **T**   **F**

2. The *Sunnah* is the action of Rasulullah ﷺ.   **T**   **F**

3. Sahih al-Bukhari and Sahih al-Muslim are
   the revelation from Allah ﷻ.   **T**   **F**

4. Good intentions will be rewarded.   **T**   **F**

5. Intentions must be spoken and not remain
   in the hearts.   **T**   **F**

6. It is allowed in Islam to have the intention
   to harm our neighbors.   **T**   **F**

Activity 2

What is the Qur'an?
What is a *Hadith*?
Let's find out how they are different.

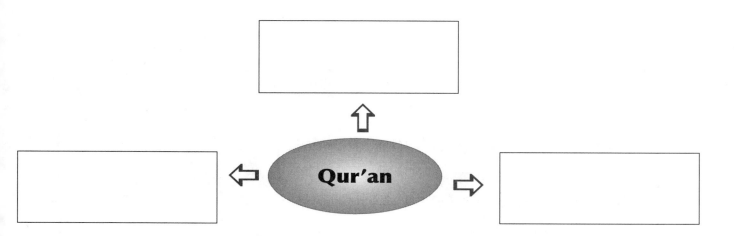

How are they different?

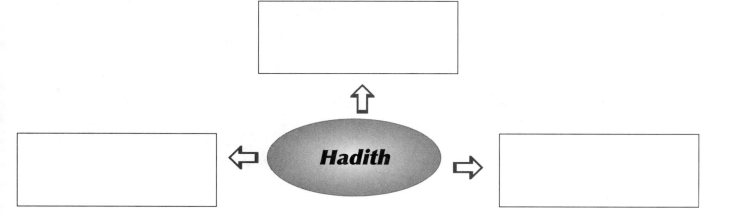

Activity 3

Allah ﷻ made intentions an important part of our worship. We should always have good intentions.

Write the good intention for doing the following actions.

Activity 4

Find all the words in the word search.

Use the clues at the bottom of the page to help you.

		2	3			
			A			
5		**W**				
			A			
1	**T**		**T**			
4	**U**					

1. Across: The feelings we have in our hearts.

2. Down: The words of Allah ﷻ.

3. Down: The written teachings of Rasulullah ﷺ.

4. Across: The actions of Rasulullah ﷺ.

5. Across: A gift from Allah ﷻ for doing good deeds.

131

Unity in the Community

Activity 1

Write about what you have learned in the spaces below.

1. All human beings are one family. Why?

2. Muslims belong to a special community. Why?

3. The Muslim *Ummah* has a special mission. What?

4. Allah ﷻ provided believers with guidance. What?

5. Our community has to be together. Why?

Activity 2

The Muslims are one *Ummah*. What does this mean?

Write about the mission of the Muslim *Ummah* in the graphic organizer.

Muslims are a special *Ummah* because they have a special mission.

What are the things our *Ummah* must do?

Invite Good Deeds	Forbid Wrong Deeds	(pick your own choice)
• _____ _____	• _____ _____	_____ • _____
• _____ _____	• _____ _____	_____ • _____

What do we need to do in order to succeed in our mission?

_____

_____

Lesson 33

Activity 3

**We are one *Ummah*. We are created by One God.
Allah ﷻ said in the Qur'an:**

> "Verily, this *Ummah* of yours is a single *Ummah* and
> I am your Lord and Creator therefore worship Me
> alone."
>
> (*al-Anbiya* 21: 29)

Write 3 things you understand from this verse.

1. _____

2. _____

3. _____

Activity 4

There are smaller words hiding in each of the words below. Can you find them?

1. h u m a n   ⇨   <u>   an, man   </u>

2. *s u n n a h*   ⇨   <u>   </u>

3. w o r s h i p   ⇨   <u>   </u>

4. m i s s i o n   ⇨   <u>   </u>

5. g u i d a n c e   ⇨   <u>   </u>

6. a b o u t   ⇨   <u>   </u>